Paper Playtime

by SADAMI YAMADA
Professor of Art at Tamagawa University

JAPAN PUBLICATIONS TRADING COMPANY

Translated by Richard L. Gage
Photographs by Ihei Misaki

First Edition, 1966

Library of Congress Catalog Card No. 66-22391

Published by
JAPAN PUBLICATIONS TRADING COMPANY
Tokyo, Rutland, Vt., New York

Printed in Japan

MAKE YOUR OWN PET ZOO
The Easy Paper-Playtime Way!

In *Paper Playtime* you will find lots of ways to make pretty animals out of only one sheet of paper. You can color them anyway you want and stand them up on your desk where they will look colorful and gay, and be fun to play with.

All the animals in this book are easy to make. Just fold a piece of paper in half, or glue it together the way the directions show, then draw an animal on it, and cut it out. Here is a hint: you will cut your animals better if you move the paper to make curved lines instead of moving the scissors.

There are beautiful colored pattern pages in this book. Cut them out on the dotted line, and fold them the way the instructions show. Then cut out the pattern. Half of the animal is already colored; you color the other half any way you want. When you have made all of the pattern-page animals, get some clean white sheets of ordinary paper, fold them the way the charts tell you, and make lots more funny paper pets.

Folding and cutting lines:

A line like the ------------- means to make a valley fold.
A line like the · — · — · — means to make a peak fold.
A line like the _____ means to cut.

Contents

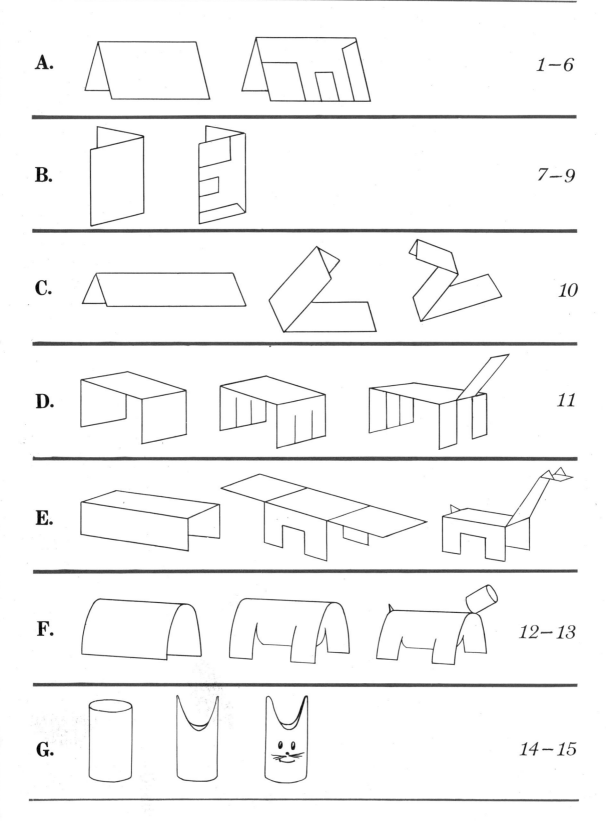

A. Begin playing with paper by folding a piece in half like this and seeing what you can make out of it.

1. Draw the lines, and cut out.
2. You have made something that looks like an animal.
3. Let's try to make a polar bear.

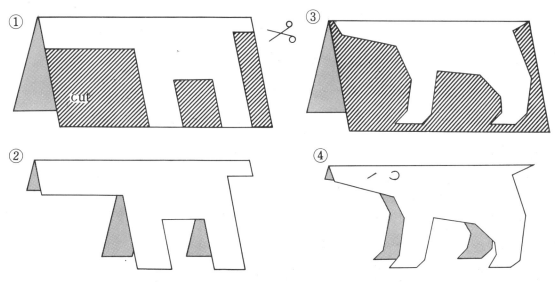

Polar bears don't mind the cold. Anyway, that's what we're told!

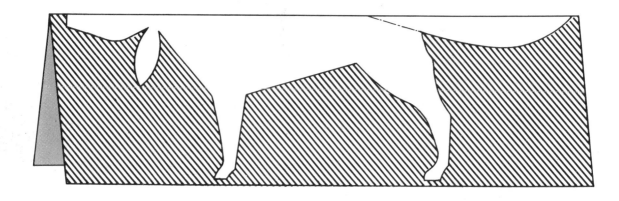

1. Carefully fold the paper in half.
2. Draw and cut out the dog shape. You'll cut better if you move the paper, *not* the scissors.
3. Fold the ears up.
4. Fold the tail on the dotted line.
5. Color your dog the way you like.

**Fold the paper, draw, and cut
Poodle, colley, or plain mutt!**

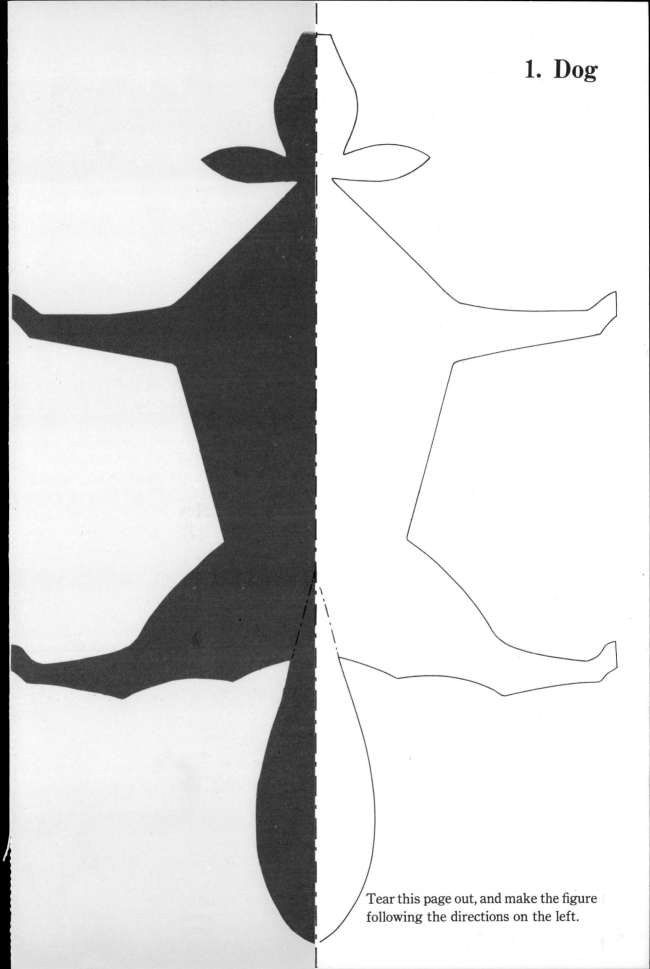

1. Dog

Tear this page out, and make the figure
following the directions on the left.

1. Fold the paper in half, draw the lines shown in chart 1, and cut them out with scissors.
2. You have made something that should remind you of some four-legged animal.
3. Fold a piece of drawing paper in half, draw in the rabbit in chart 3, and cut it out with scissors.
4. Fold the ears up on the dotted lines.

A

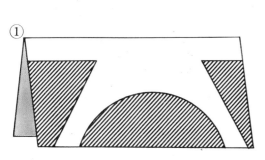

①

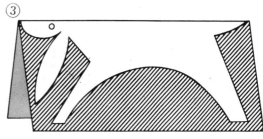

③

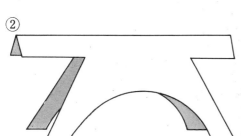

②

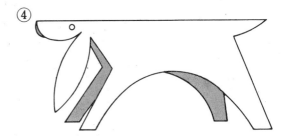

④

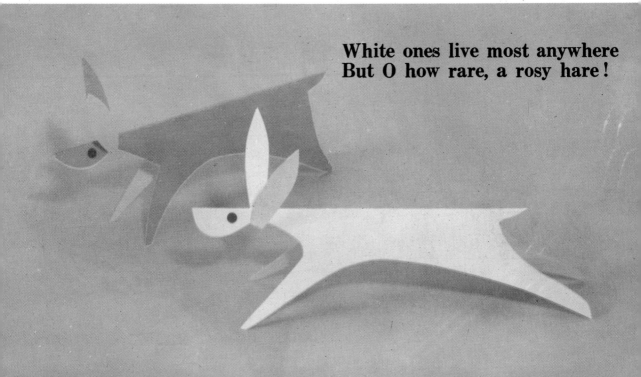

**White ones live most anywhere
But O how rare, a rosy hare!**

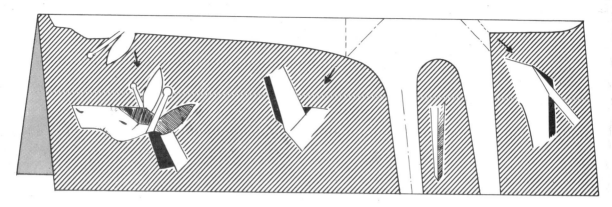

1. Fold a piece of paper carefully in half, and draw in the figure of a giraffe. Cut it out with scissors on the solid lines.

2. Using your fingertips, fold the head, ears, and tail up as the chart indicates.

3. Crease each of the legs as the chart shows to make them strong enough to support the weight of the figure.

When I try to rhyme giraffe
All I do is laugh and laugh!

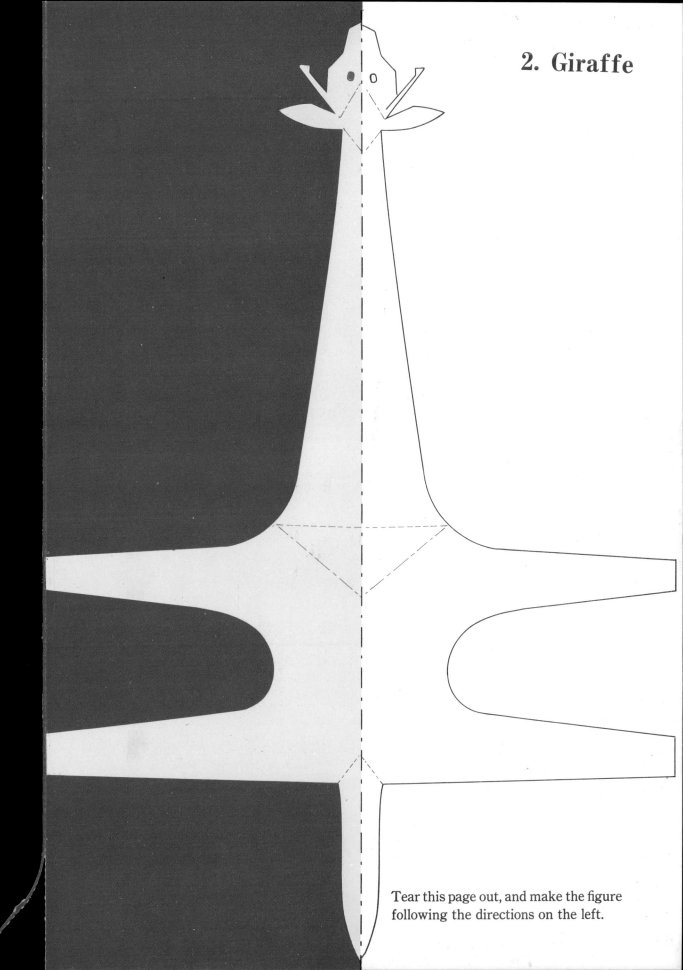

2. Giraffe

Tear this page out, and make the figure
following the directions on the left.

①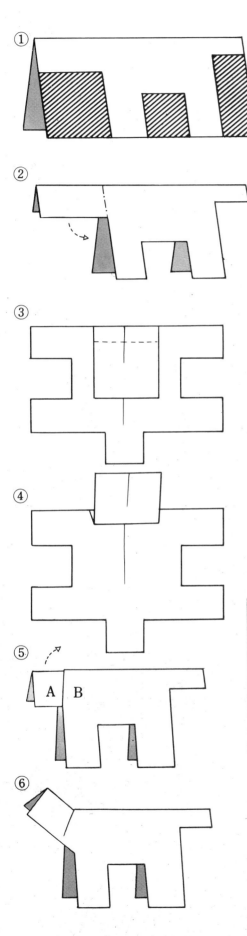

②

③

④

⑤ A B

⑥

A

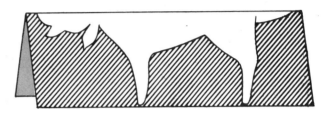

1. Fold a piece of paper in half, and cut on the lines shown in chart 1.

2. This form should look like some sort of animal to you.

3. Open the figure flat, fold the neck in as the dotted line in chart 1 shows, and then, leaving a little of it folded in, fold it out again. Hold A and B tightly in your fingers, and pull A upward for a good neck.

**Hubby Bill and wifey Nan
Munch and crunch an old tin can!**

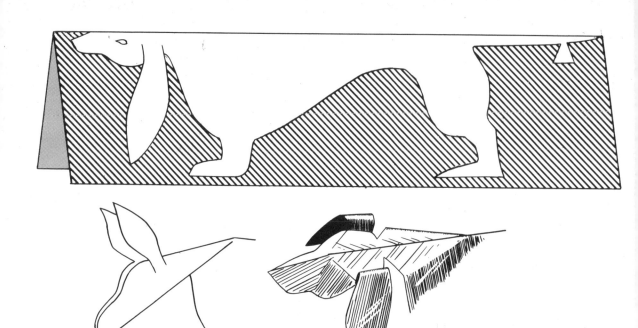

(making the head section)

1. Fold the paper, and cut on the solid lines.
2. Join the paper, and fold the neck over frontward on the dotted line.
3. Fold it backward on the same line to make the neck crease.
4. Crease the head into shape, and fold the ears to the shape the chart shows.

Coat is brown, eye is round,
Tummy's low, low to the ground.

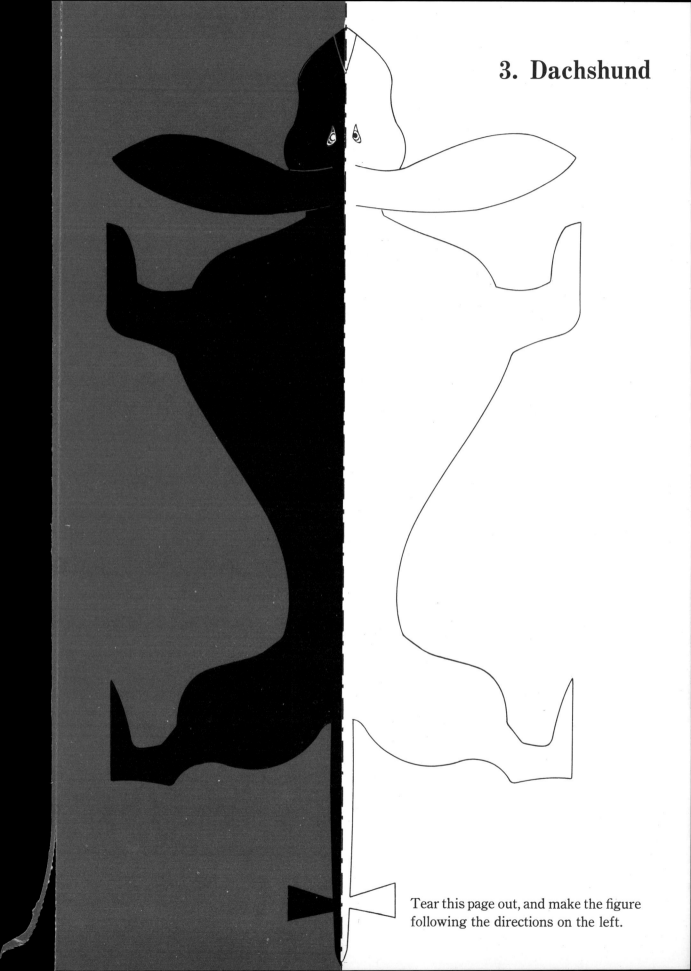

3. Dachshund

Tear this page out, and make the figure following the directions on the left.

A

1. Fold your paper in half this way.
2. Draw the water buffalo in the chart, and cut him out.

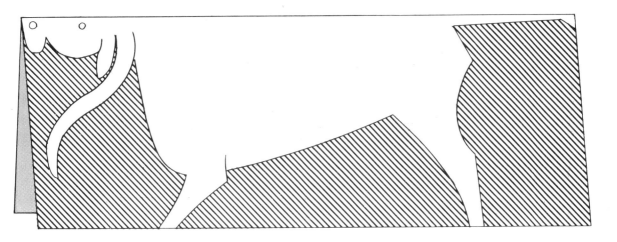

His horns are long, but my how slow
Moves the water buffalo!

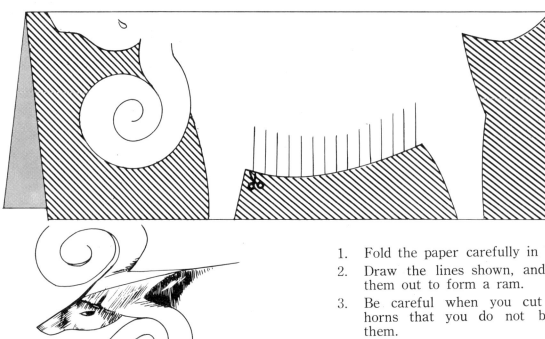

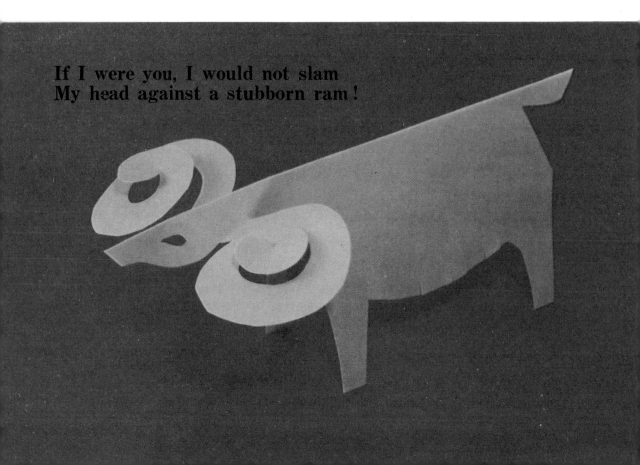

(making the head section)

1. Fold the paper carefully in half.
2. Draw the lines shown, and cut them out to form a ram.
3. Be careful when you cut the horns that you do not break them.
4. Cut the fringes of wool on the ram's stomach.
5. Hold the head in the fingers of your left hand and the neck in the fingers of your right hand, and flatten the top of the head into the triangular shape in the chart.

**If I were you, I would not slam
My head against a stubborn ram!**

4. Ram

Tear this page out, and make the figure
following the directions on the left.

1. Carefully fold your paper in half.
2. Draw in the lion, and cut it out.

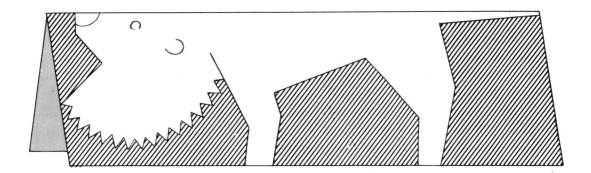

Lion lyin' in the grass,
Are you laddy?   Are you Lass?

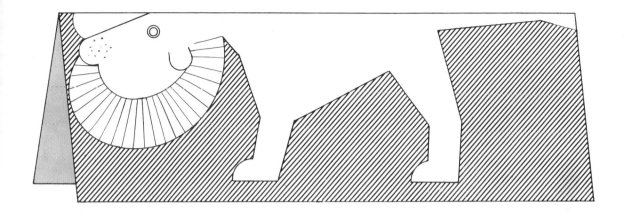

1. Carefully fold a piece of paper in half.
2. Cut on the solid outlines.
3. Cut the lines in the lion's mane.
4. Fold the head and shoulders as the dotted lines show.
5. You may either draw in the nose and eyes or cut them from paper of another color and paste them on.

**Laddy lions two, its plain.
Lady lions lack a mane!**

1. Bring corners A and B of a square of paper into the center line as you see in the chart.
2. Fold the piece of paper in half on the dotted line.
3. Leaving the paper folded, cut through all layers on the line the chart shows. Make the wings by folding parts C and D up on the dotted lines.

A

①

②

③

④

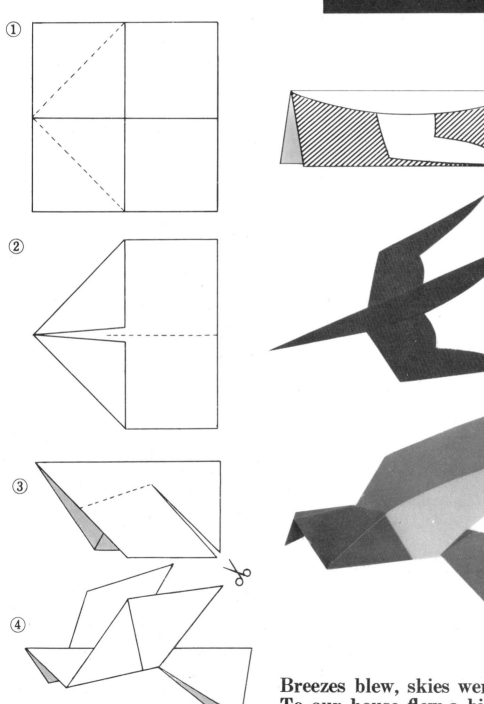

Breezes blew, skies were blue,
To our house flew a bird, blue too.

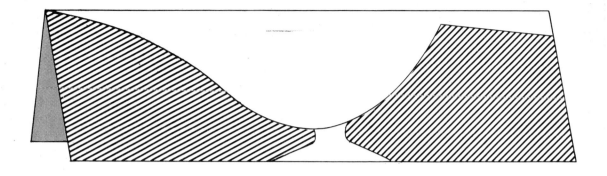

1. Carefully fold a piece of paper in half.
2. Cut out the bird outline you see in the chart.
3. Use your imagination, and color in eyes and bright gay wings.

Of lots of kinds of birds I've heard,
But, really, this bird is absurd!

6. Dodo

Tear this page out, and make the figure
following the directions on the left.

B. Now fold your piece of paper this way and have some more fun!

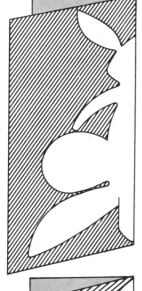

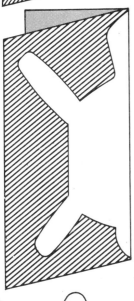

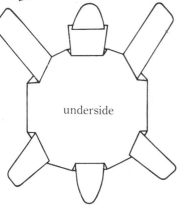

underside

First fold the turtle's legs in once then out again for the shape in the chart.

They say the turtle's steady pace
Outdid the rabbit in the race.

(making the tail)

1. Fold paper in half.
2. Draw in the kangaroo, and cut it out.
3. Fold the tail as the chart shows.

**I tell you true, I would not boo
Or say pooh pooh to a kangaroo!**

7. Kangaroo

Tear this page out, and make the figure
following the directions on the left.

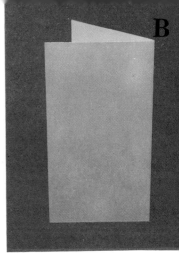

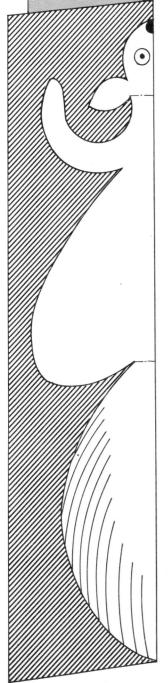

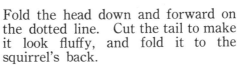

Fold the head down and forward on the dotted line. Cut the tail to make it look fluffy, and fold it to the squirrel's back.

**Had you a tail, would you unfurl
Your curly tail like the little squirrel?**

1. Carefully fold a piece of paper in half.
2. Cut out on the outlines.
3. Fold part A to the front to complete the head and ear-like feathers.
4. Fold the legs first up then down as the chart shows.
5. Color the entire body just like an owl, but leave the whites of the eyes bright white.

Does the wise old owl seem wise to you?
Always asking "Who, who, whoooooooooo?"

8. Owl

Tear this page out, and make the figure following the directions on the left.

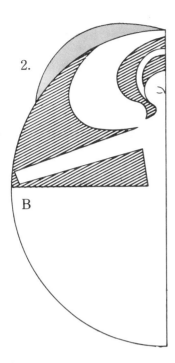

2.

B

B

Fold a circle of paper in half, and cut out the angel's outline.

1. Glue parts A and A′ together.
2. Glue parts B and B′ together.

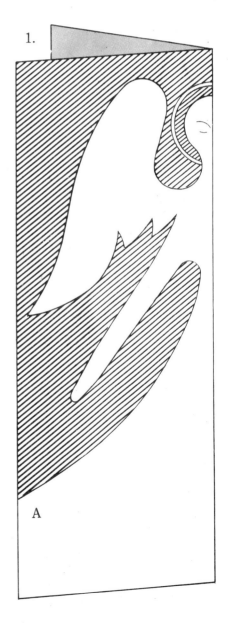

1.

A

1. Fold a piece of paper carefully in half.
2. Cut out on the outlines.
3. Glue the two lowest edges of the skirt together to form a ring.
4. Bring the hands forward, and glue them together.
5. Make the halo of a separate piece of paper, and glue it to the back of the head.

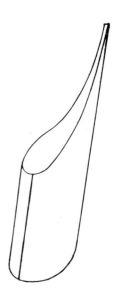

**What better guard all through the night
Than angels on your left and right?**

9. Angel

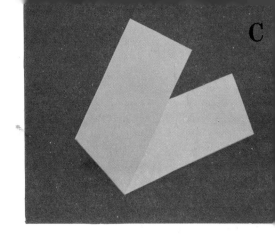

C.

C. When we fold a piece of paper as you see in the photograph we make a shape that reminds us of some sort of animal. What do you suppose it is? Let's play with the paper some more and see what we can make.

①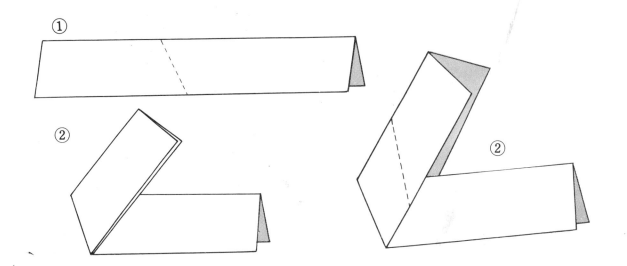

②

②

③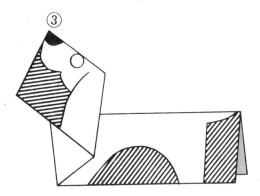

**You'd run and play without fail
If this pup would wag his tail.**

1. Leave the first fold folded, and make a crease. Fold the paper inside out on the crease in chart 2.

2. If you fold 2′ forward on the dotted line, the paper looks even more like an animal. Try cutting the outlines you see in 3.

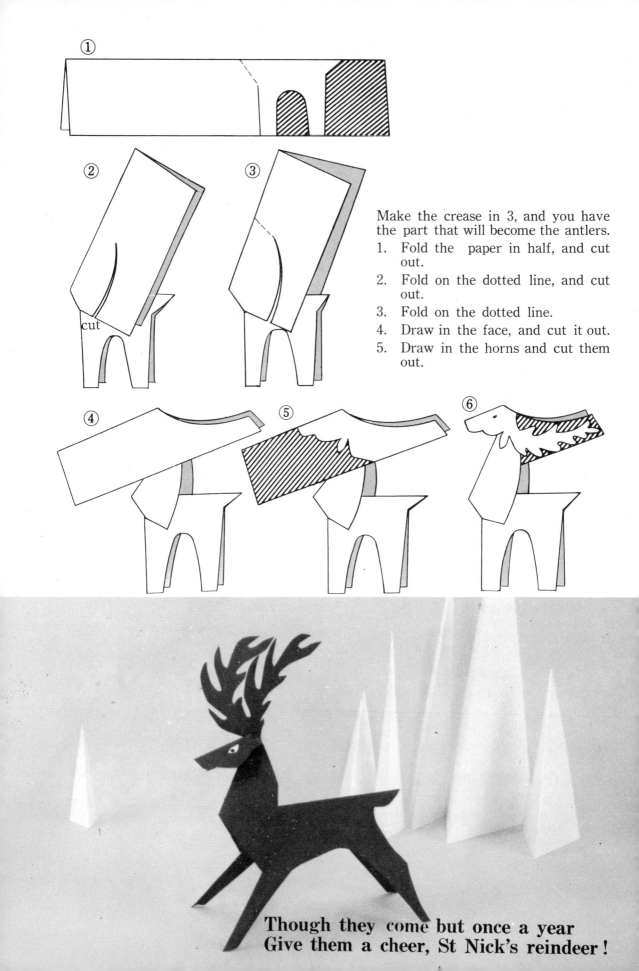

Make the crease in 3, and you have the part that will become the antlers.

1. Fold the paper in half, and cut out.
2. Fold on the dotted line, and cut out.
3. Fold on the dotted line.
4. Draw in the face, and cut it out.
5. Draw in the horns and cut them out.

**Though they come but once a year
Give them a cheer, St Nick's reindeer!**

10. Reindeer

Tear this page out, and make the figure
following the directions on the left.

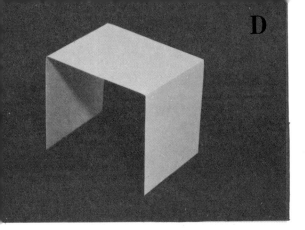

D   **E**

Make a short table, and cut like this.

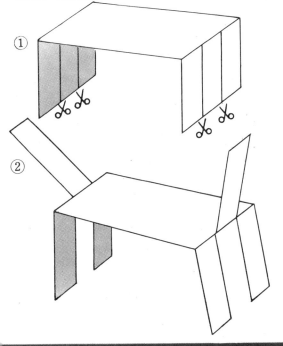

① ②

Make a long table, and cut like this.

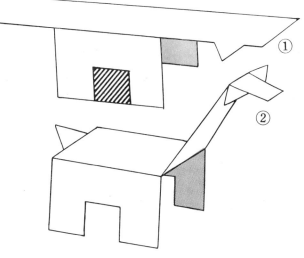

① ②

Try different ways of cutting the leg sections of the table, and you will be able to make shapes that remind you of animals.

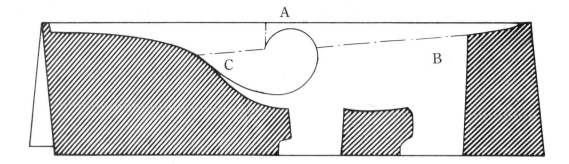

1. Fold a piece of paper in half, but do not make a firm crease.
2. Cut out on the outlines.
3. Make the head shape by folding down part A on the dotted line. Lightly crease the ears into place on line C.

4. Lightly crease the back on line B on both sides of the figure. Be sure you make the back look like the one in the model.
5. Lightly shape the trunk into a curved line.

Can you say, I'll bet you can't,
Who's mighty as the elephant?

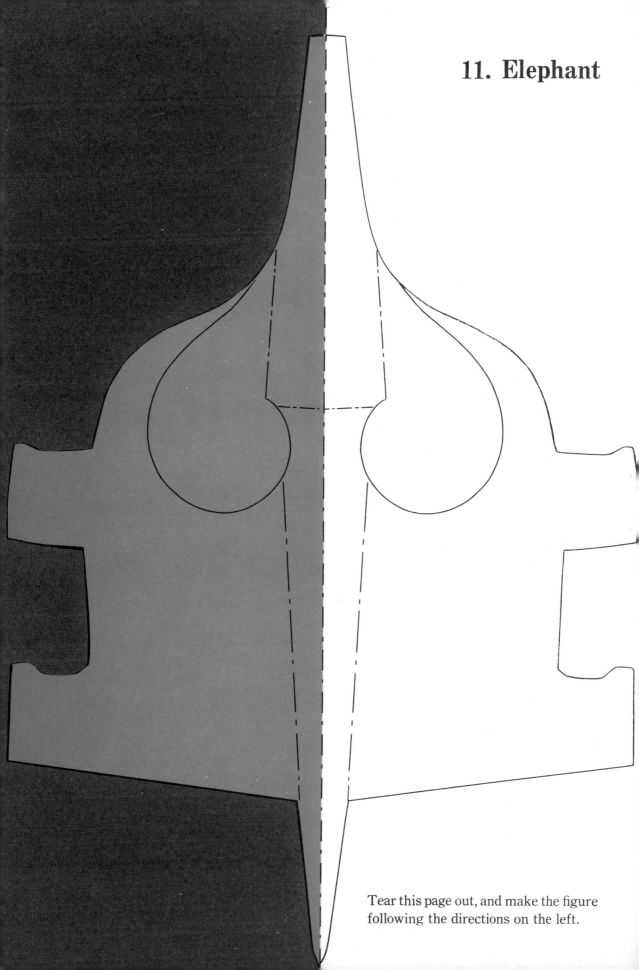

11. Elephant

Tear this page out, and make the figure following the directions on the left.

F. Stand a piece of paper this way, and you'll be able make even better animals.

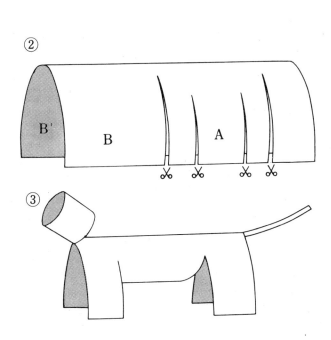

② B' B A

③

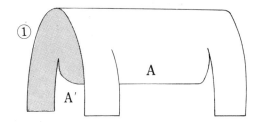

① A A'

1. If you make an arch of a piece of paper and cut as the chart shows then bring parts A and A' together underneath to make a circle you have something that looks very much like an animal.

2. Make a tunnel of a long narrow piece of paper, and then, thinking about where you want the head, the legs, the tail, etc. make cuts at the right places like the ones in the chart. If you then glue parts A and A' together underneath you form the animal's body. If you glue parts B and B' together on the top you make the animal's head.

I don't think he could say bow wow; A dog like this one won't know how!

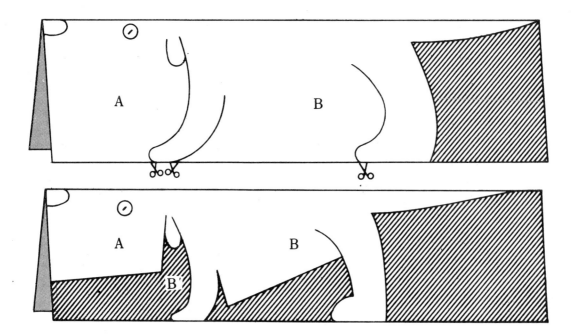

1. Glue together parts A and A'.
2. Glue together parts B and B'.
3. When you first fold the paper in half do not make a firm crease, but let the animal's back round naturally.

Paper tigers are all right,
But real ones give you quite a fright!

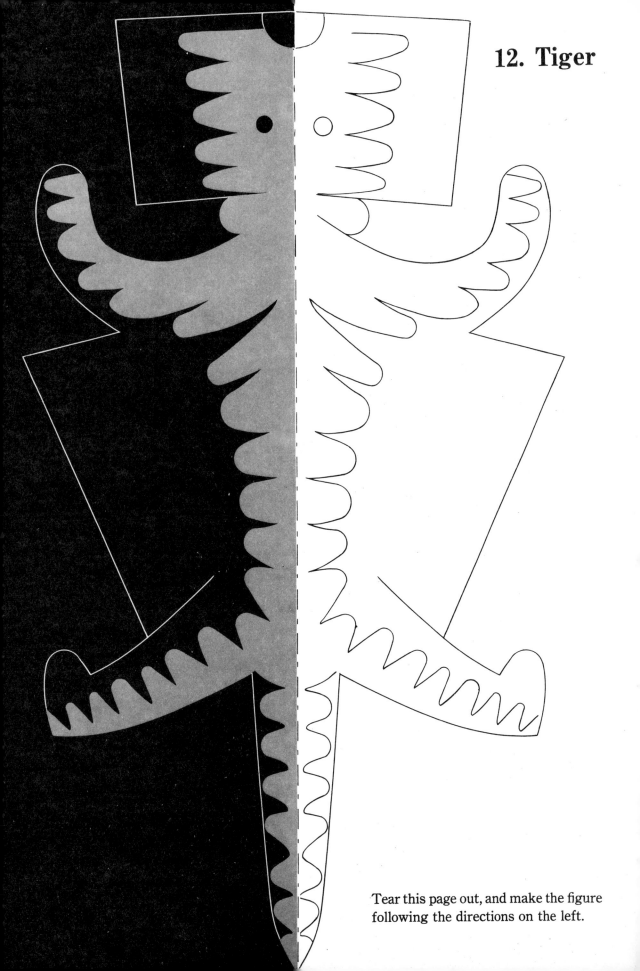

12. Tiger

Tear this page out, and make the figure
following the directions on the left.

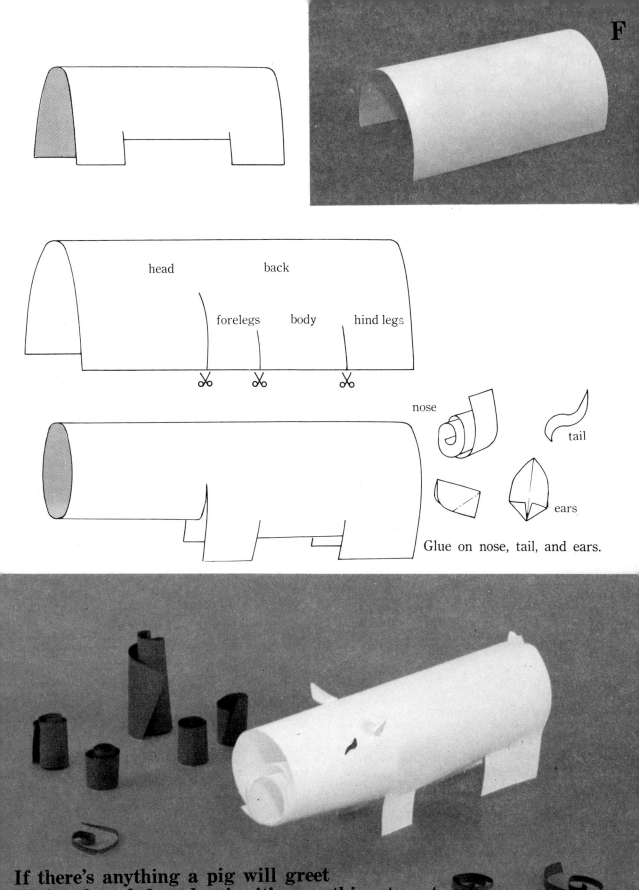

F

head　　　　back

forelegs　　body　　hind legs

nose

tail

ears

Glue on nose, tail, and ears.

If there's anything a pig will greet
With a broad, broad grin, it's something to eat.

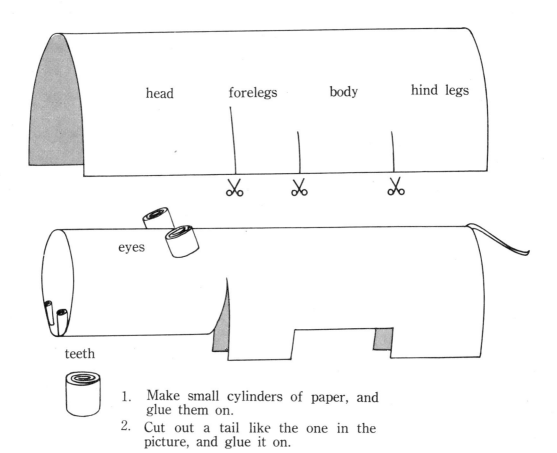

head   forelegs   body   hind legs

eyes

teeth

1. Make small cylinders of paper, and glue them on.
2. Cut out a tail like the one in the picture, and glue it on.

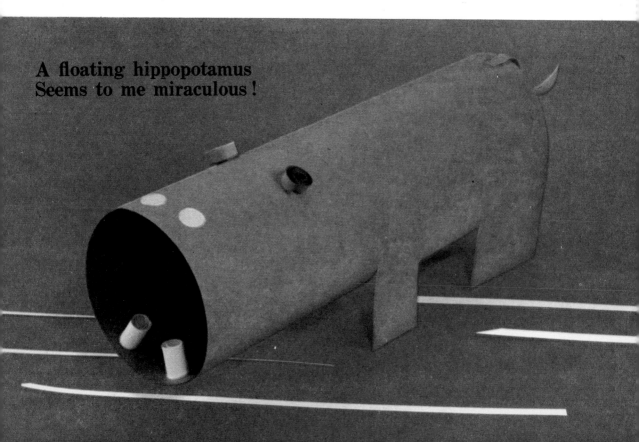

**A floating hippopotamus
Seems to me miraculous!**

13. Hippopotamus

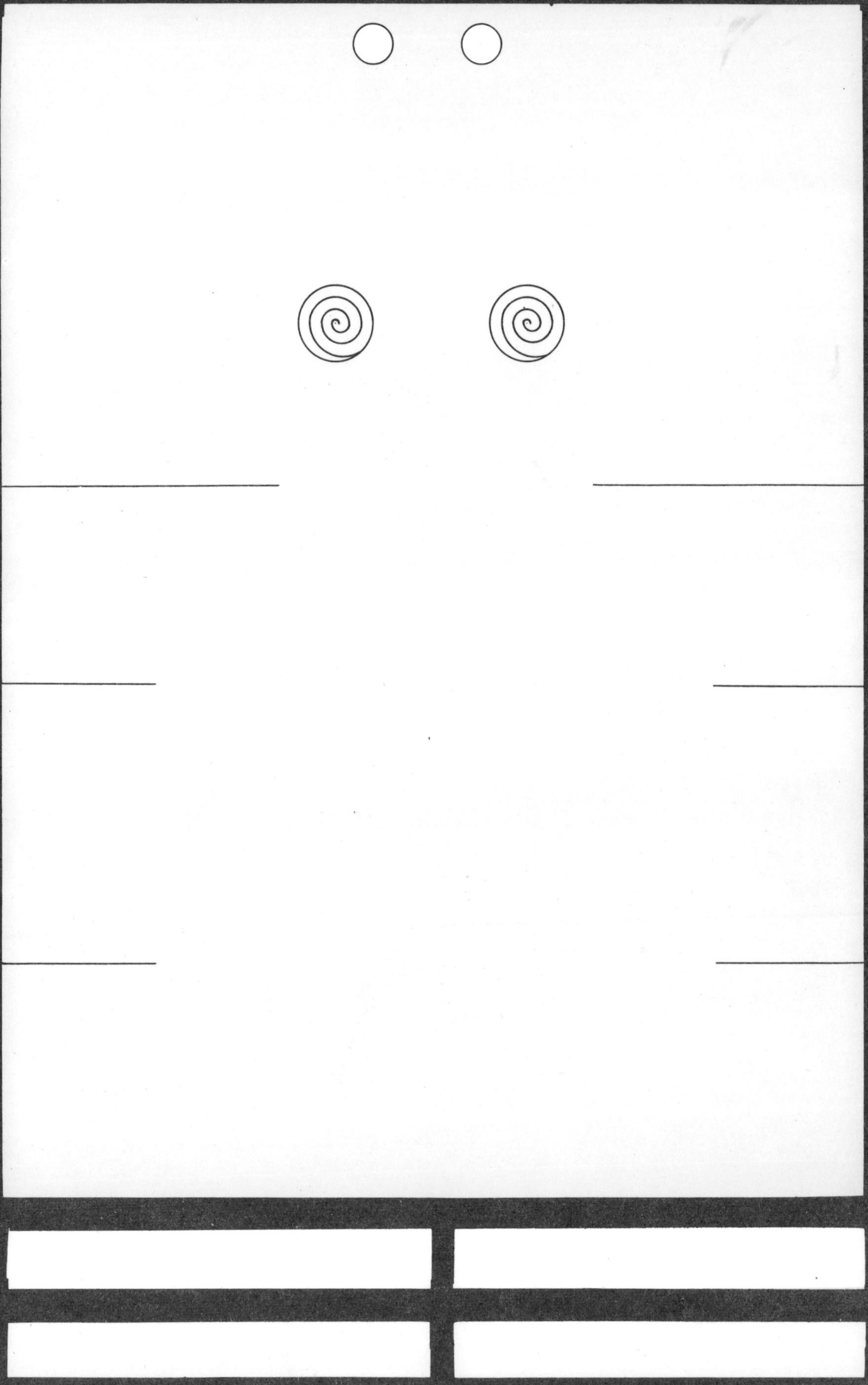

G. Glue a piece of paper together like this, and try to make the things you see on these pages.

1. Cut out beak, color it yellow, fold it, and glue it on.
2. Cut out wings, and color them a black.

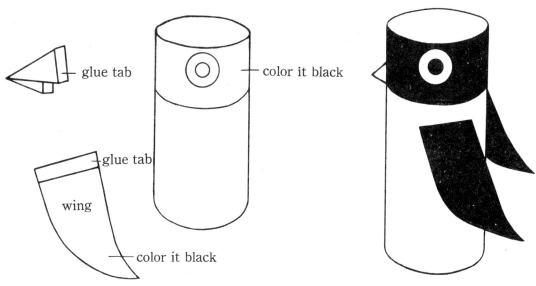

glue tab

color it black

glue tab

wing

color it black

**Blue-eyed penguins in a row,
All dressed up, no place to go!**

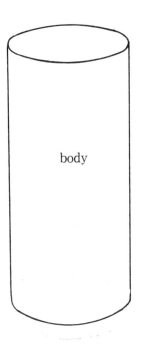

body

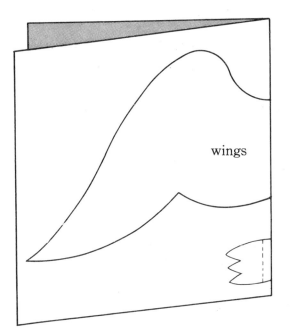

wings

1. Make the body of a paper cylinder.
2. Make the wings and feet, and glue them on.
3. Draw the face in.

Up all night, asleep all day!
Fine for owls, but not our way.

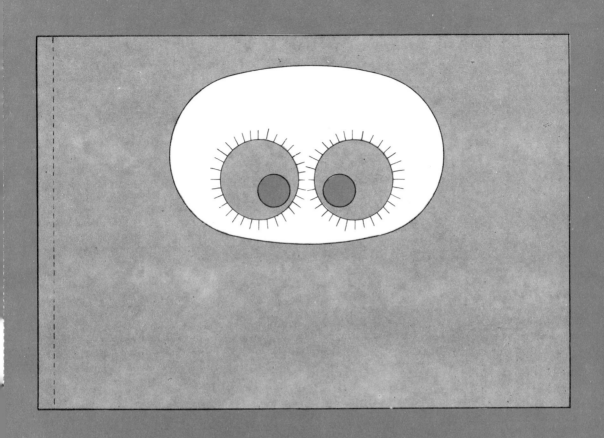

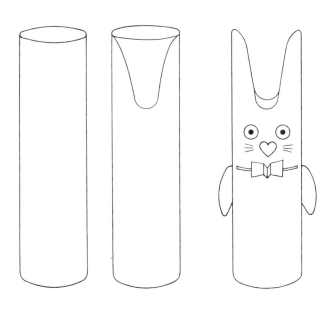

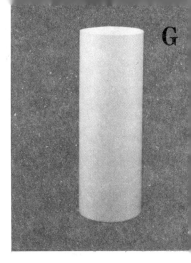

1. Cut a flat sheet of paper like this.
2. Glue it together on the edges to look like this.
3. Cut out eyes, heart-shape nose, and bowtie. Glue them on.
4. Draw in whiskers.

**Who lays the eggs for Easter Day,
The chicken or the bunny, pray?**

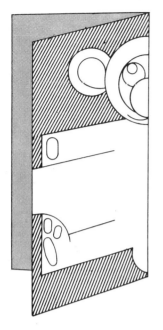

1. Carefully fold a piece of paper in half.
2. Cut out the figure in the chart.
3. Bring parts A and A′ to the front, and glue them together.

To disagree you may be ready,
But all bears are *not* nicknamed Teddy!

15. Teddy Bear

Tear this page out, and make the figure
following the directions on the left.